NEIL A. KJOS
PIANO LIBRARY

LEVEL THREE

Sight Reading

Piano Music for Sight Reading and Short Study

By Keith Snell

ISBN-10: 0-8497-9850-7
ISBN-13: 978-0-8497-9850-4

Sight Reading (Preparatory Level through Level Ten) contains piano music of various textures and styles which may be used as a supplement to any course of study to improve sight reading, as well as overall reading skills.

"Sight reading" means playing music you have never seen before. In other words, reading music "at first sight." A good sight reader can play accurate notes, rhythms, dynamics and articulations at, or near, the given tempo. **The best way to become a good sight reader is to read new music every day**.

Here are some tips to help you progress:

Before you sight read, look through the entire piece and observe the:

- Time Signature
- Key Signature
- Clefs
- Dynamics
- Accidentals
- Slurs, Ties, Staccatos, Accents, etc.
- Rhythmic and Melodic Patterns

As you sight read:

1. Play at a slow to moderate tempo.
    - Use a metronome to help you keep a steady beat.
    - Count aloud as you play.
2. Keep your eyes on the music.
    - Avoid looking up and down from the music to your hands.
    - Look ahead in your music to see what is next.
3. Keep going, even if you make mistakes; avoid going back to fix anything.

After you sight read:

1. Evaluate your playing.
    - Were the notes and rhythms correct?
    - Were the dynamics and articulations markings clear and distinct?
    - Did the music continue to move forward as it maintained a steady beat?
2. Sight read the music again.
    - Concentrate on correcting any previous mistakes.
    - Set a goal for a perfect performance by the third reading. After playing a piece three times, you have begun to learn it, and are no longer sight reading.

Short Study pieces are meant to be practiced, but only for a few days or, at most, a few weeks. These are not designed for polishing to performance level, but instead to help you improve your ability to learn new music quickly and efficiently.

"Short study" is about the *amount of time* you spend on a piece (for example, 5 minutes a day for one week), whereas "sight reading" is about the *number of times* you play a piece (no more than three).

If you can play the pieces in this book perfectly:

- *the first time through*, you might need to go to the book at the next higher level to improve your sight reading.
- *the third time through*, you are at the right level for improving your sight reading.
- *after a few days of practice*, you are in the right level for short study music.

The music in these books (except for original music by Diane Hidy or Keith Snell) has been selected from composers of the 17th through early 20th centuries. Many of these works are not in their original form, and are sometimes extracts from longer works. They have been edited, and in some cases altered, specifically for use as sight reading exercises.

1.

Keith Snell

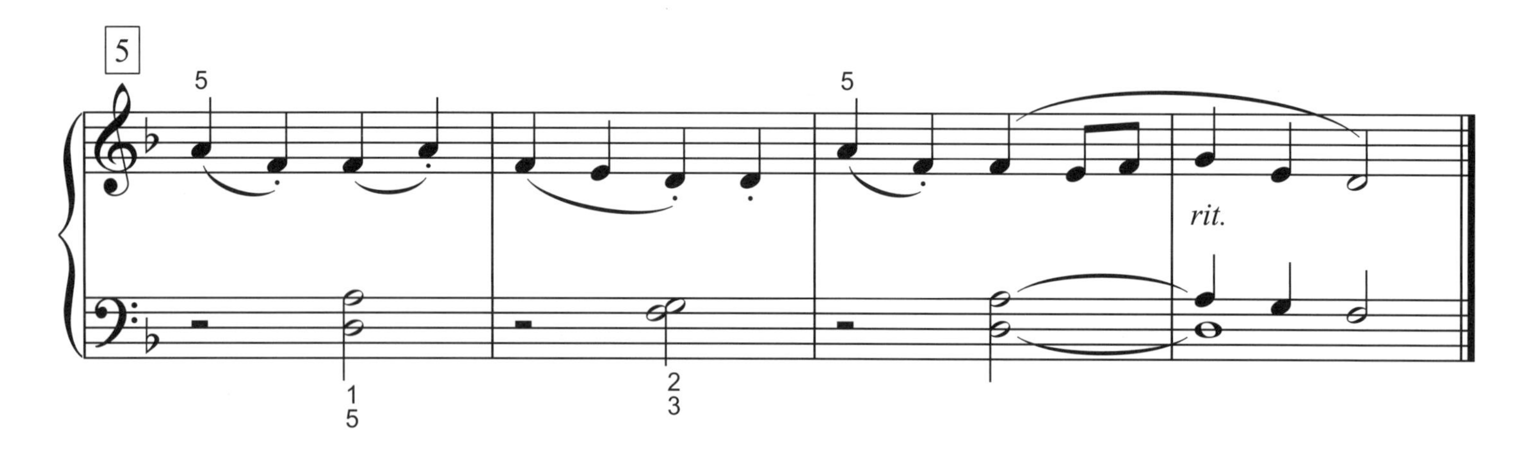

2.

Keith Snell

3.

Cornelius Gurlitt
(1820-1901)
Op. 117, No. 10

4.

Cornelius Gurlitt
Op. 82, No. 21

5.

C. V. Stanford
(1852-1924)
No. 2 from *Six Sketches*

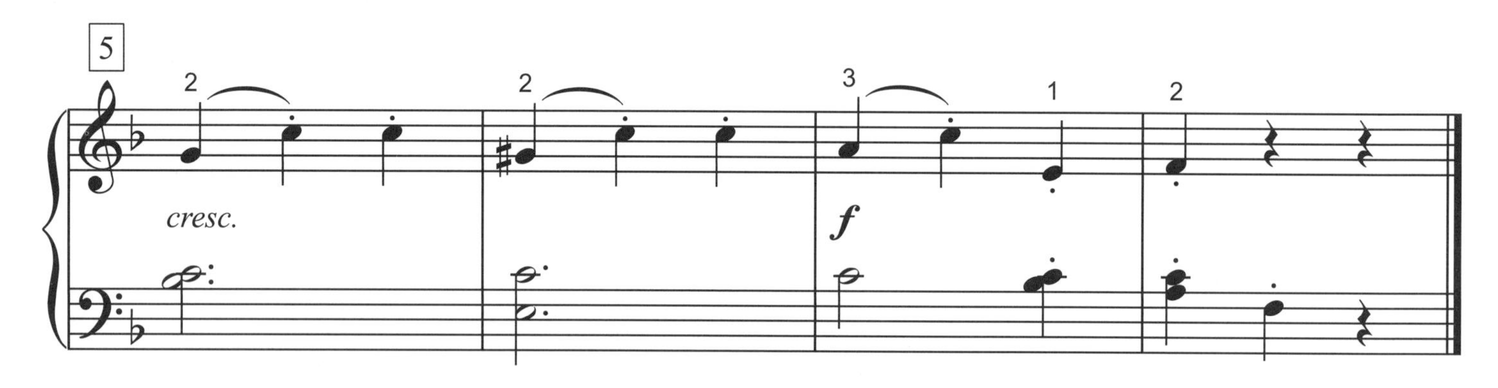

6.

Ferdinand Beyer
(1803-1863)
Op. 101, Nos. 68 & 69

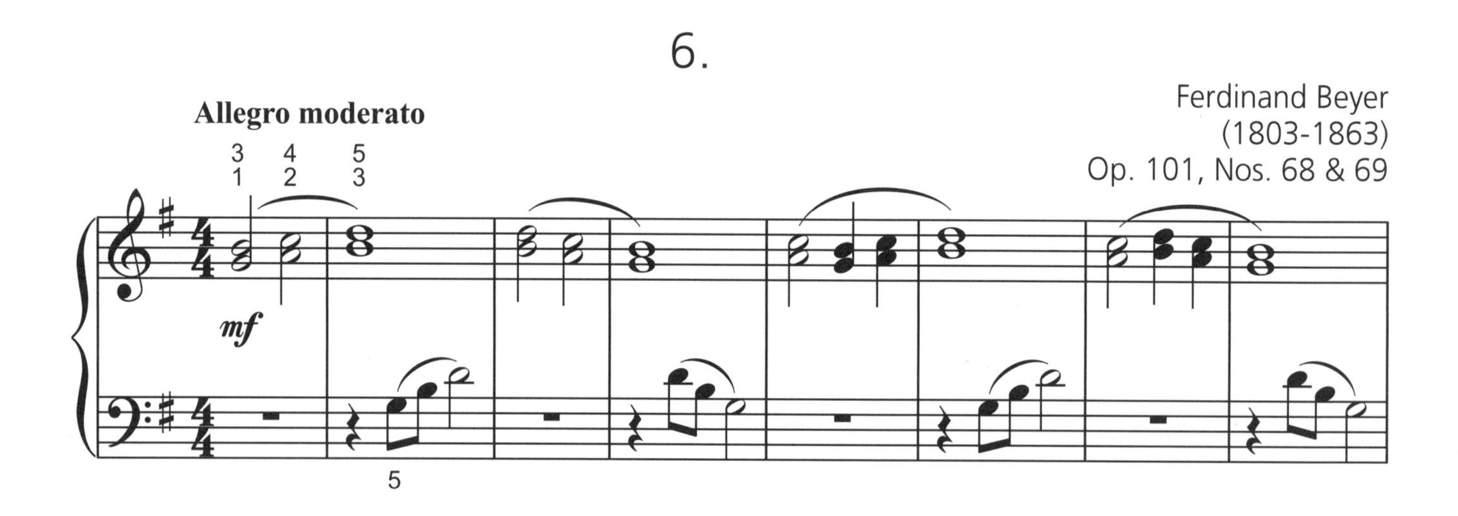

7.

Ferdinand Beyer
Op. 101, No. 29

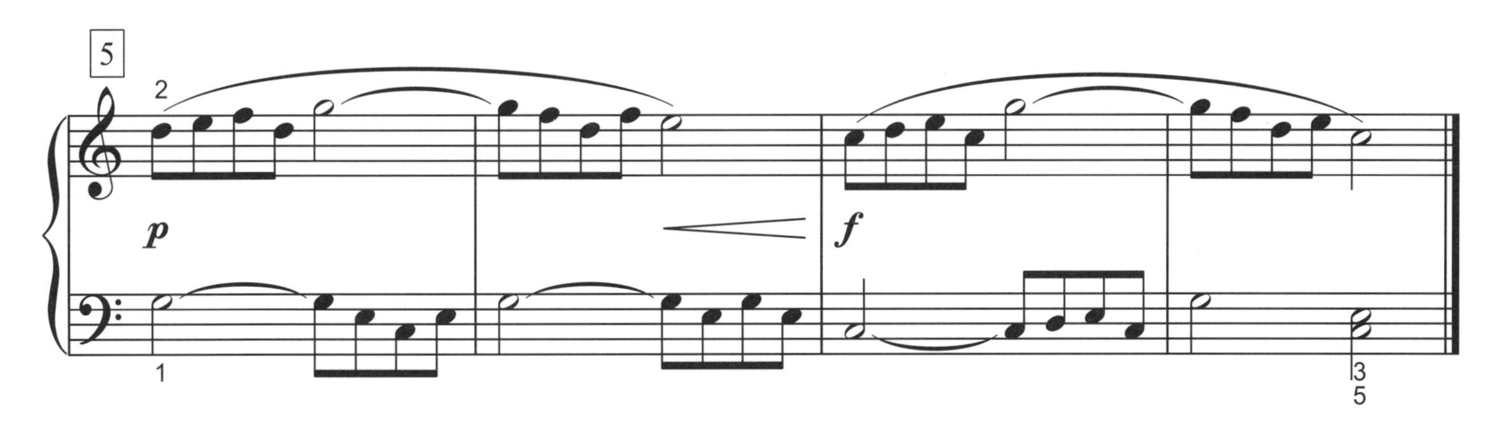

8.

Ferdinand Beyer
Op. 101, No. 22

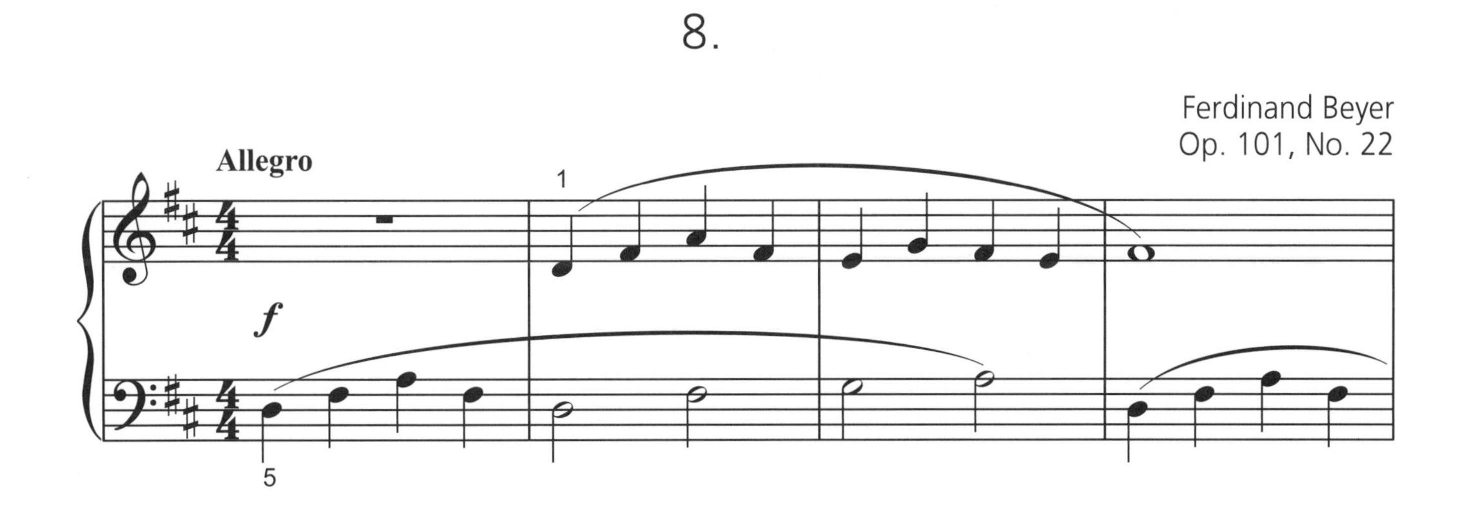

9.

Ferdinand Beyer
Op. 101, No. 25

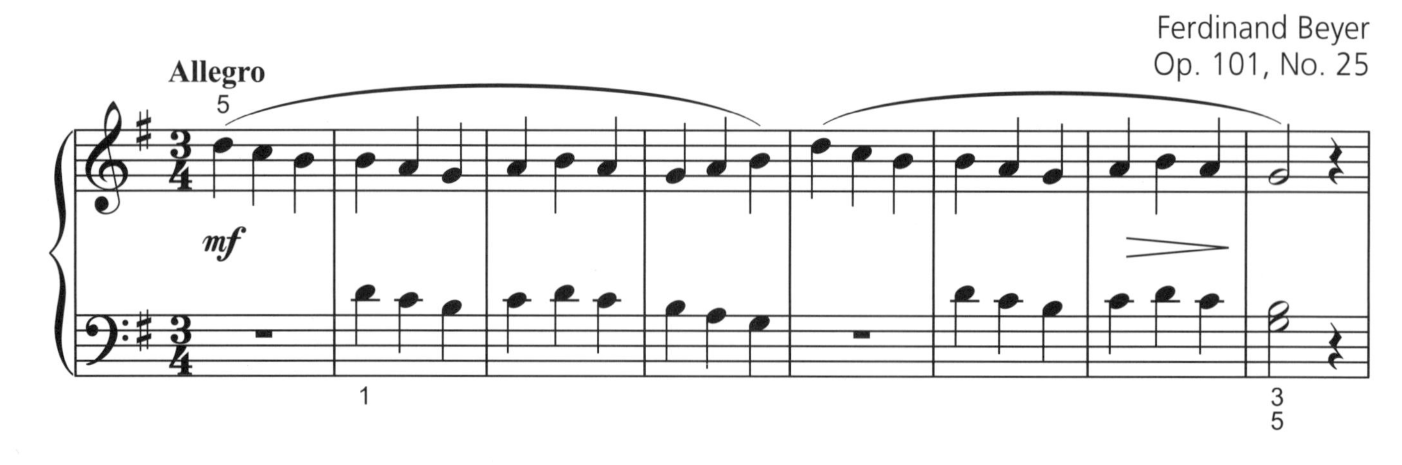

10.

Cornelius Gurlitt
Op. 82, No. 17

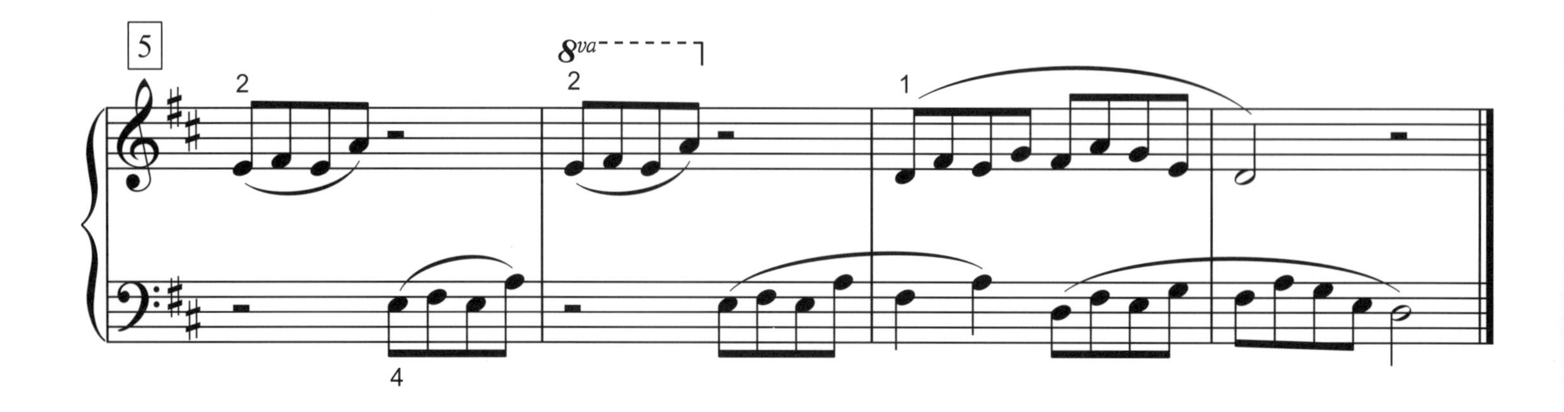

11.

Cornelius Gurlitt
Op. 187, No. 31

Béla Bartók
(1881-1945)
Sz. 53, No. 6

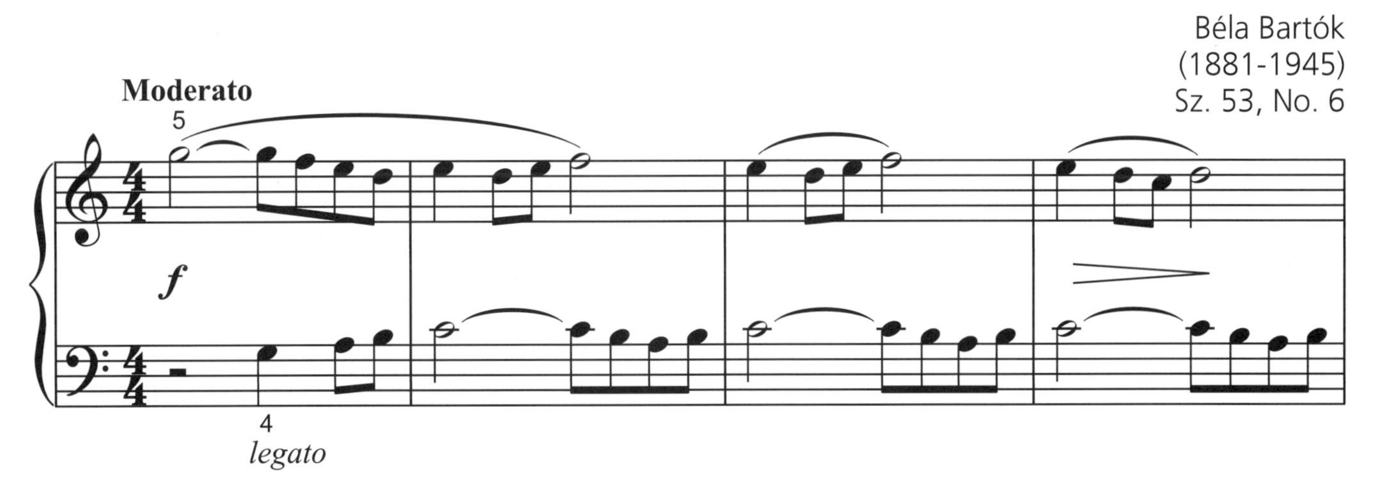

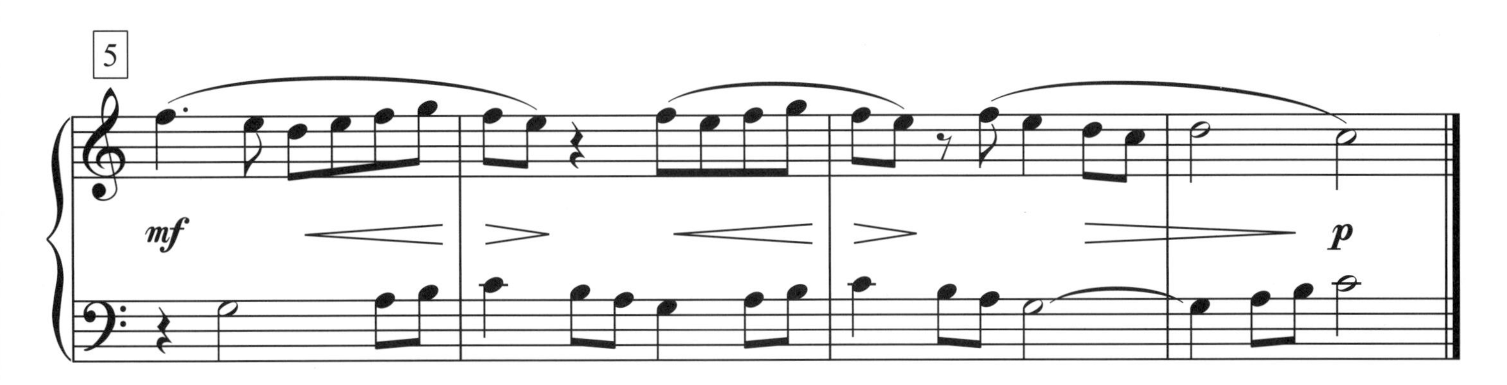

13.

Jacques Saint-Luc
(1616-1689)

Allegretto

14.

Alexander Reinagle
(1756-1809)
Op. 1, No. 5

Allegretto

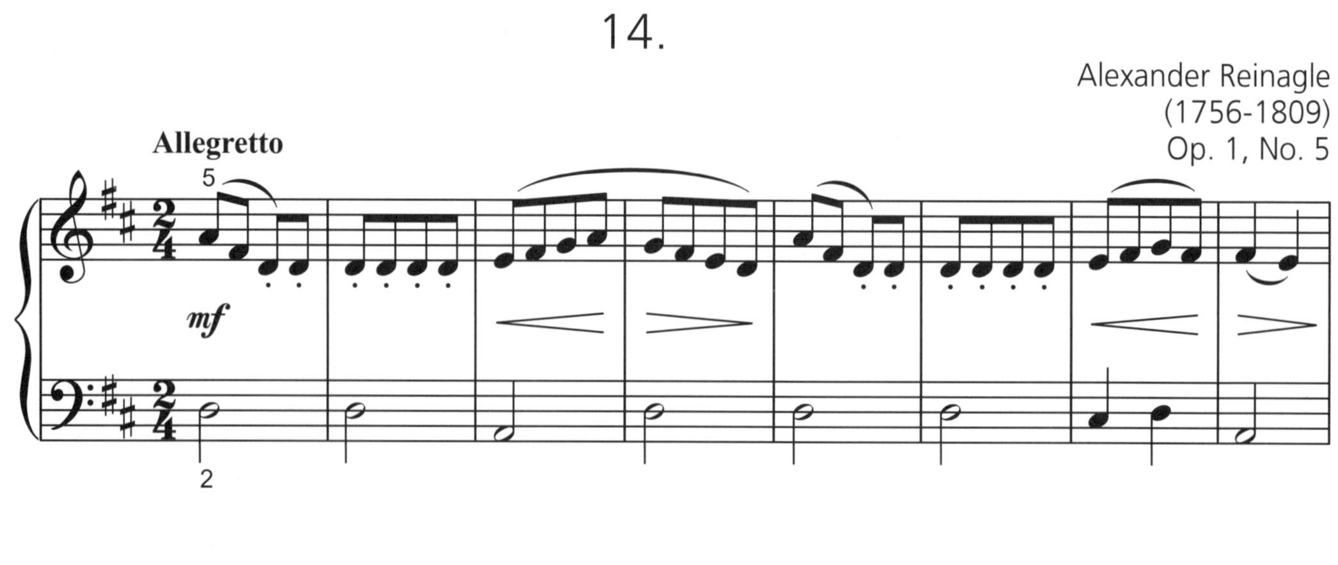

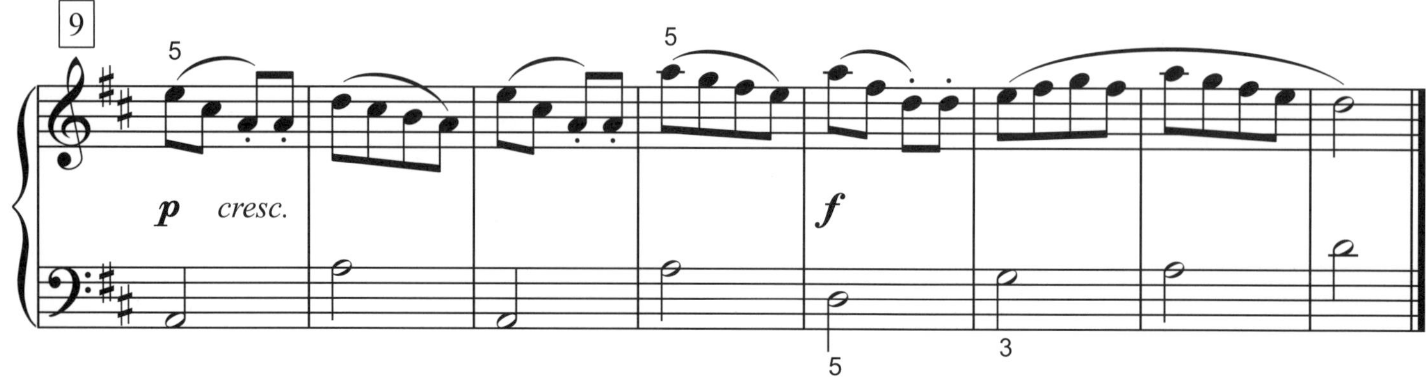

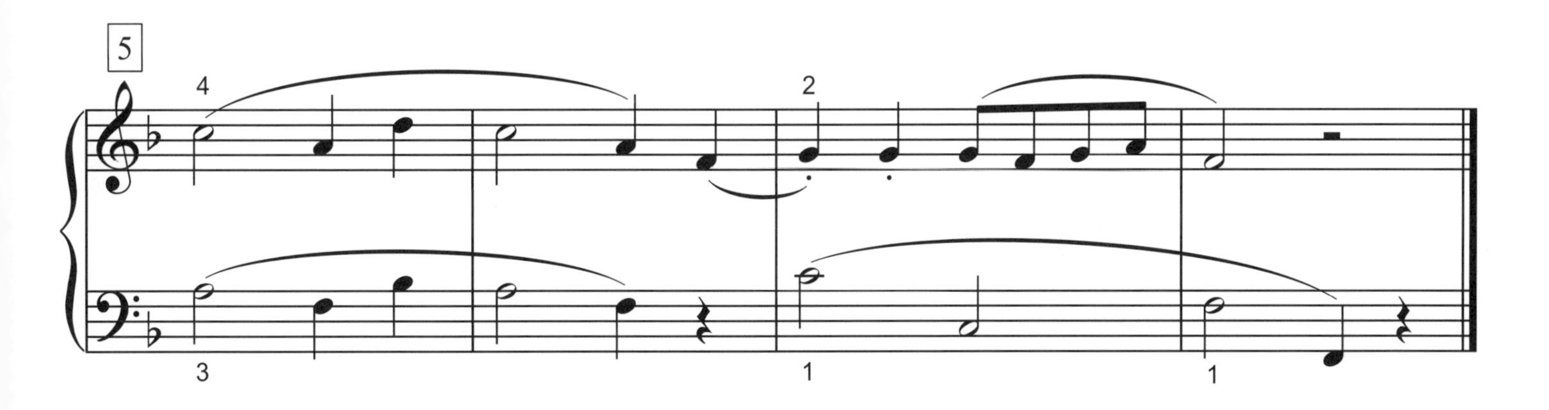

Alexander Reinagle
Op. 1, No. 7

17.

Daniel Speer
(1636-1707)

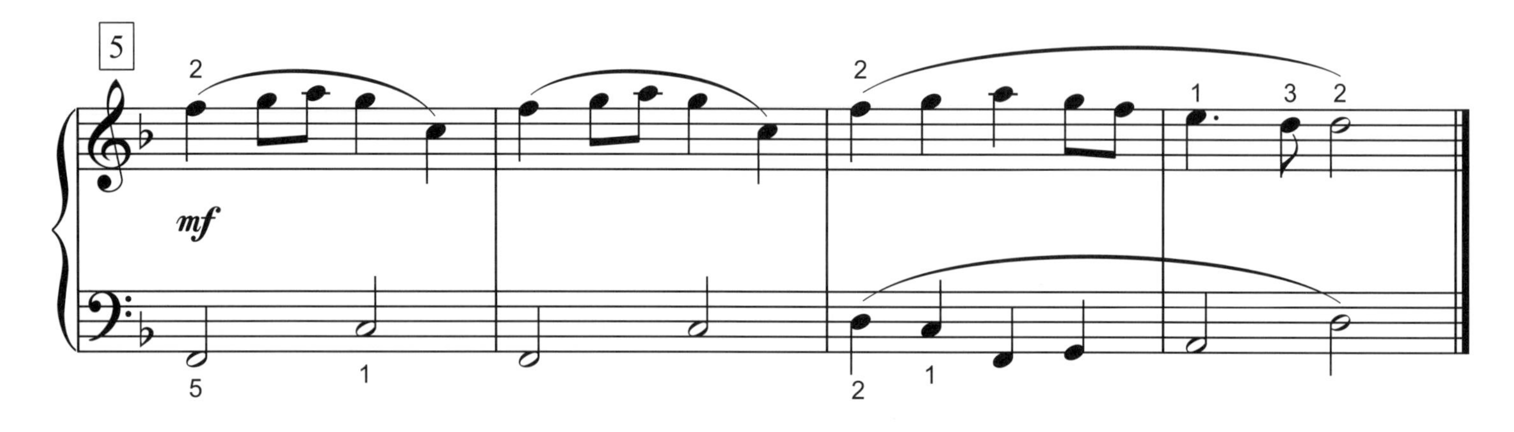

18.

George Frideric Handel
(1685-1759)

19.

Ferdinand Beyer
Op. 101, No. 54

20.

Ferdinand Beyer
Op. 101, No. 53

21.

Daniel Gottlob Türk

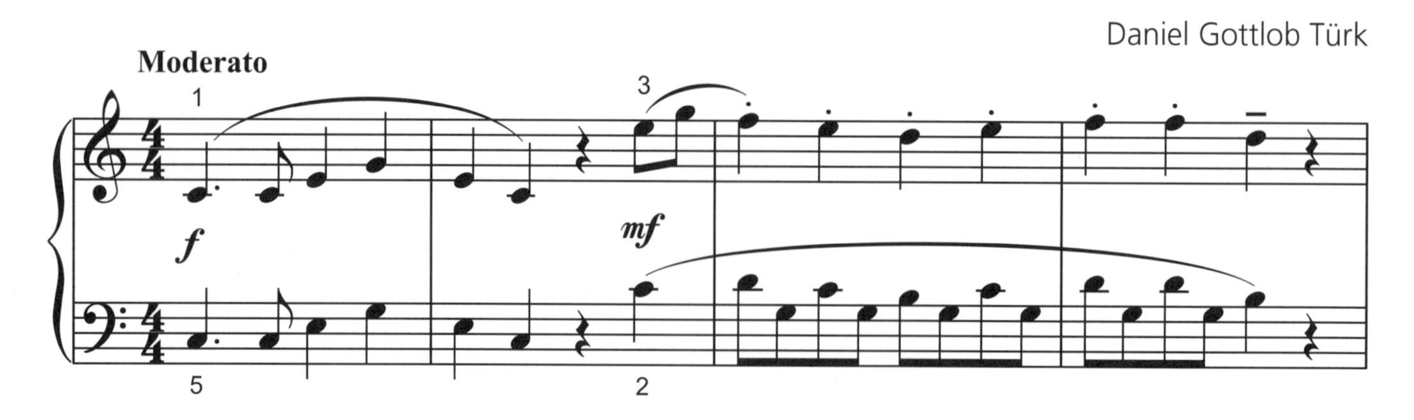

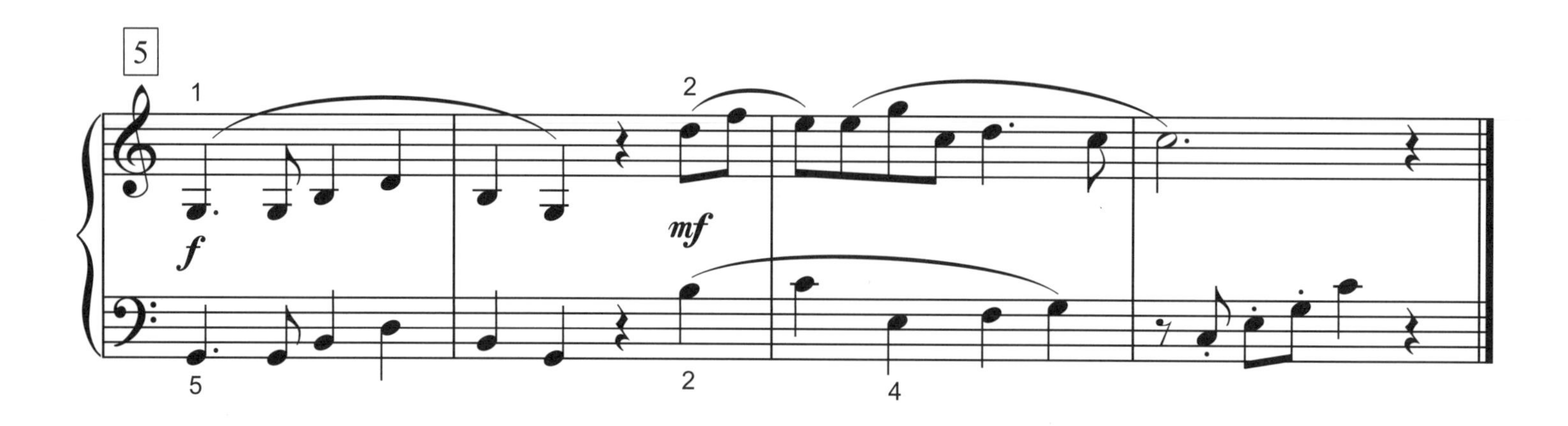

22.

István Bartalus
(1821-1899)

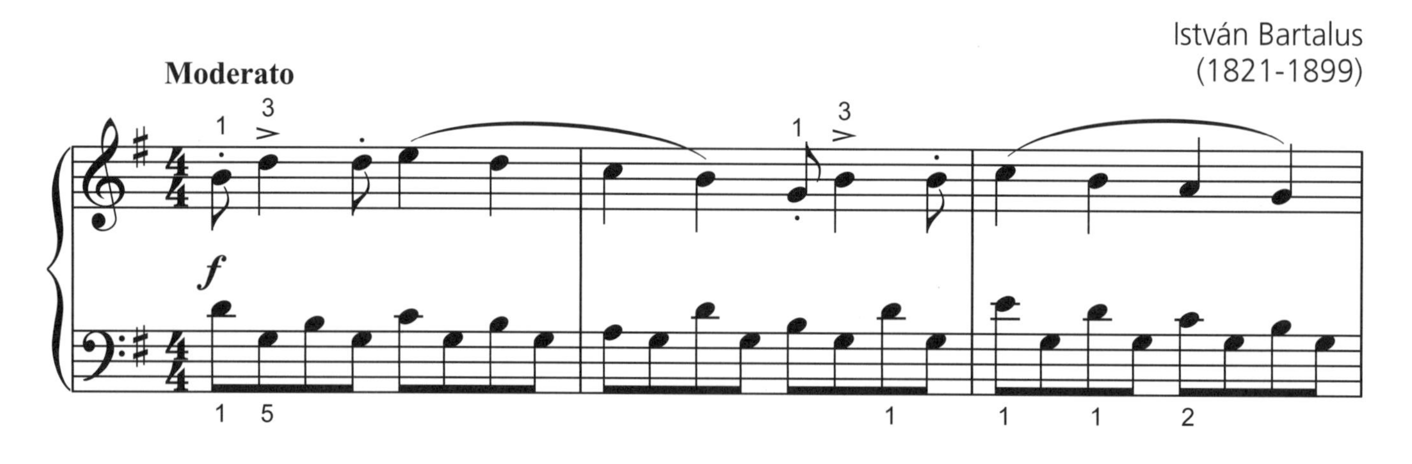

23.

Andante con moto

Daniel Speer

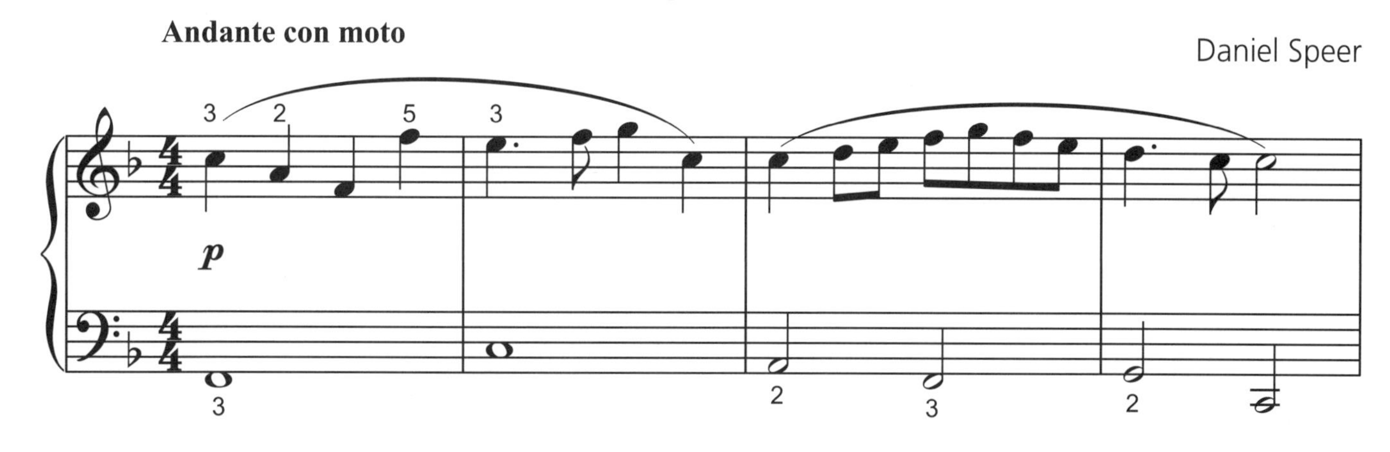

24.

Cornelius Gurlitt
Op. 82, No. 29

Andante piacavole

25.

Cornelius Gurlitt
Op. 117, No. 9

26.

Ludwig Schytte
(1848-1909)
Op. 108, No. 3

27.

Ludwig Schytte
Op. 108, No. 13

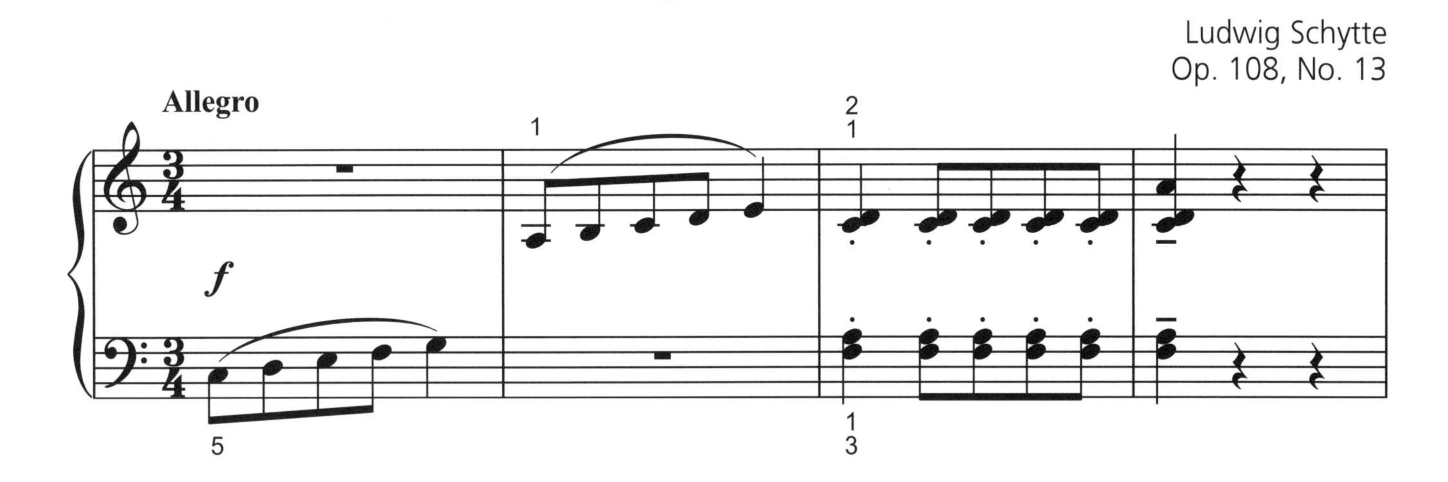

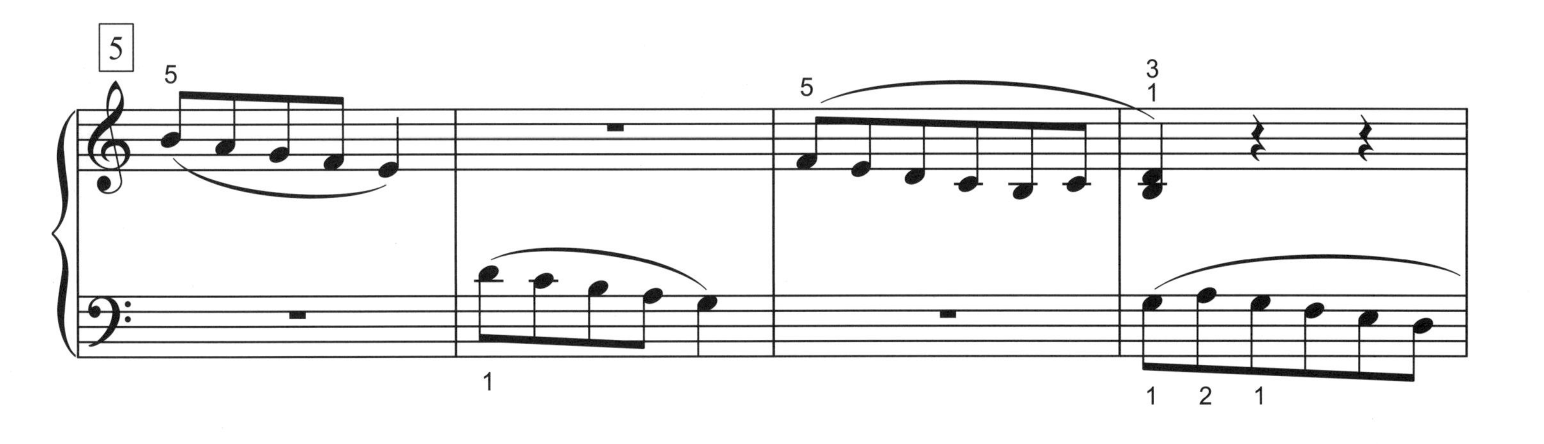

28.

Keith Snell

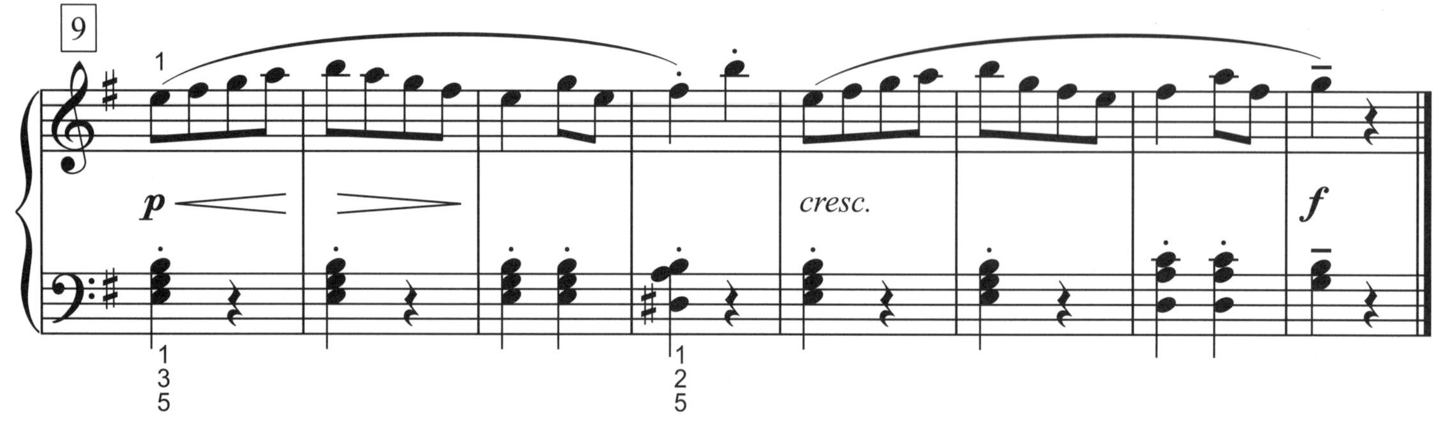

29.

August Müller
(1767-1817)

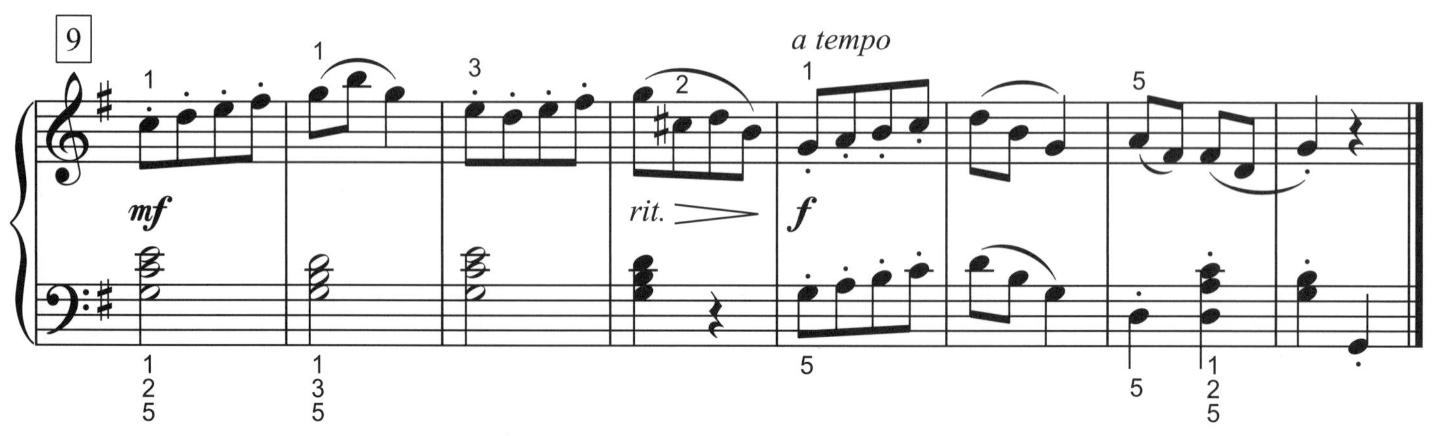

30.

Ferdinand Beyer
Op. 101, No. 20

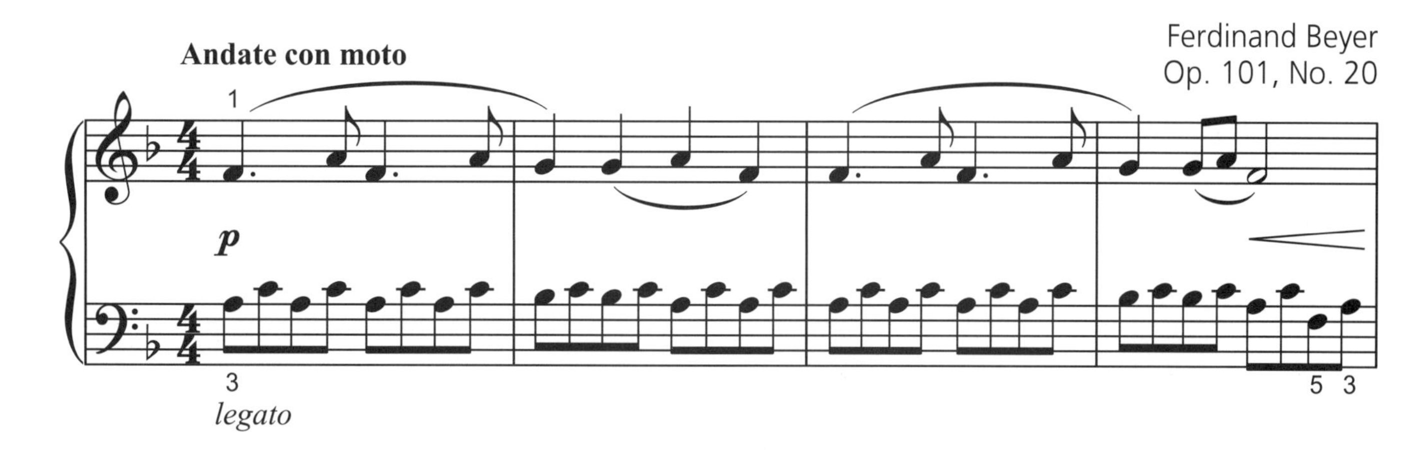

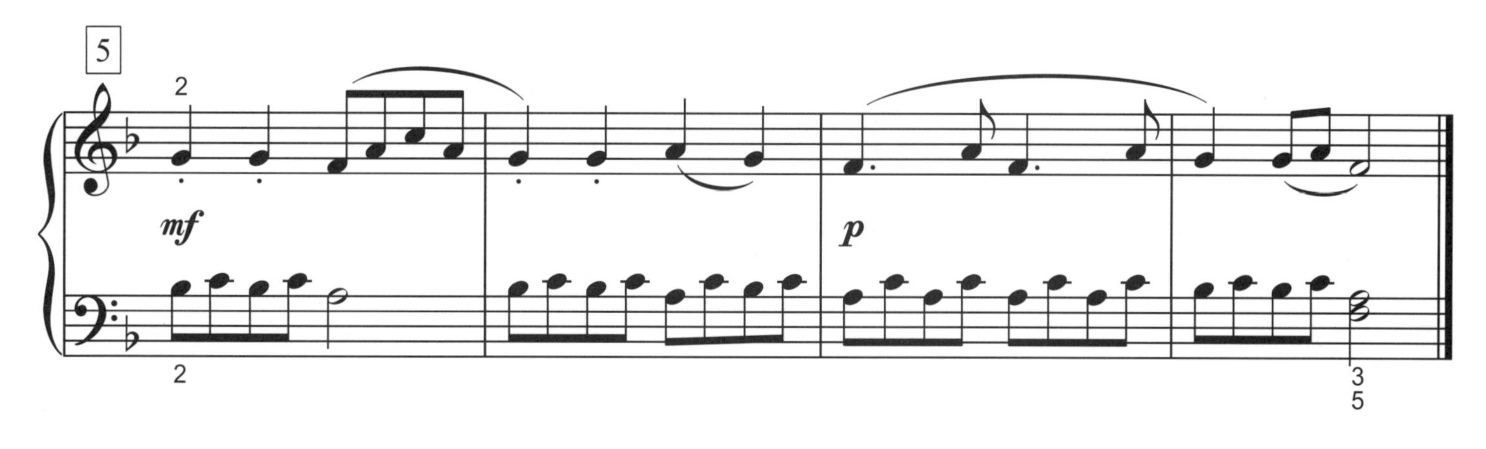

31.

Ferdinand Beyer
Op. 101, No. 49

32.

Hermann Berens
(1826-1880)
Op. 70, No. 26

33.

Hermann Berens
Op. 70, No. 17

34.

Hermann Berens
Op. 70, No. 15

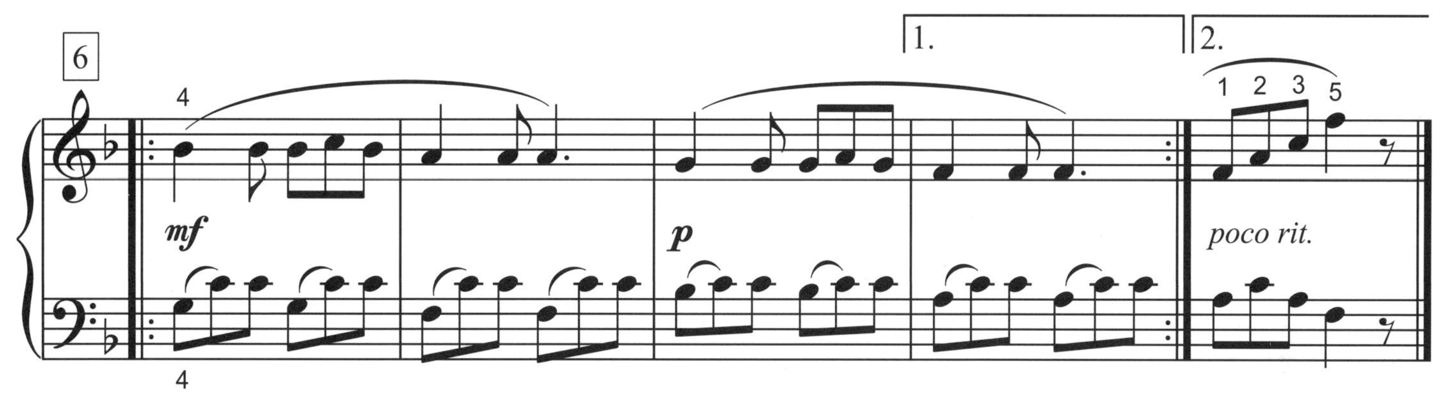

35.

Hermann Berens
Op. 70, No. 23

36.

Ferdinand Beyer
Op. 101, No. 52

37.

Ferdinand Beyer
Op. 101, No. 66

38.

August Müller

39.

Ferdinand Beyer
Op. 101, No. 57

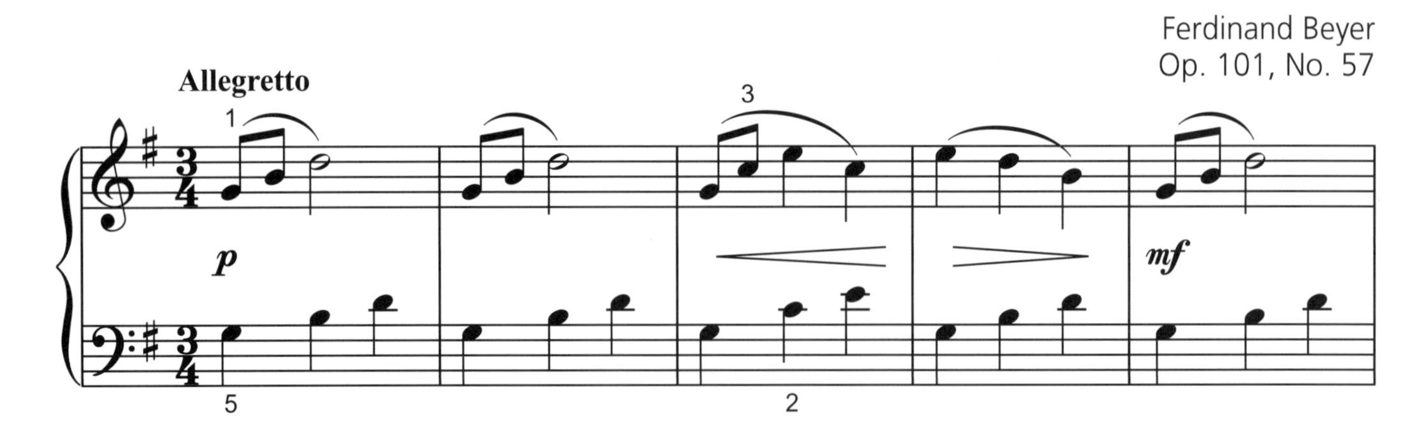

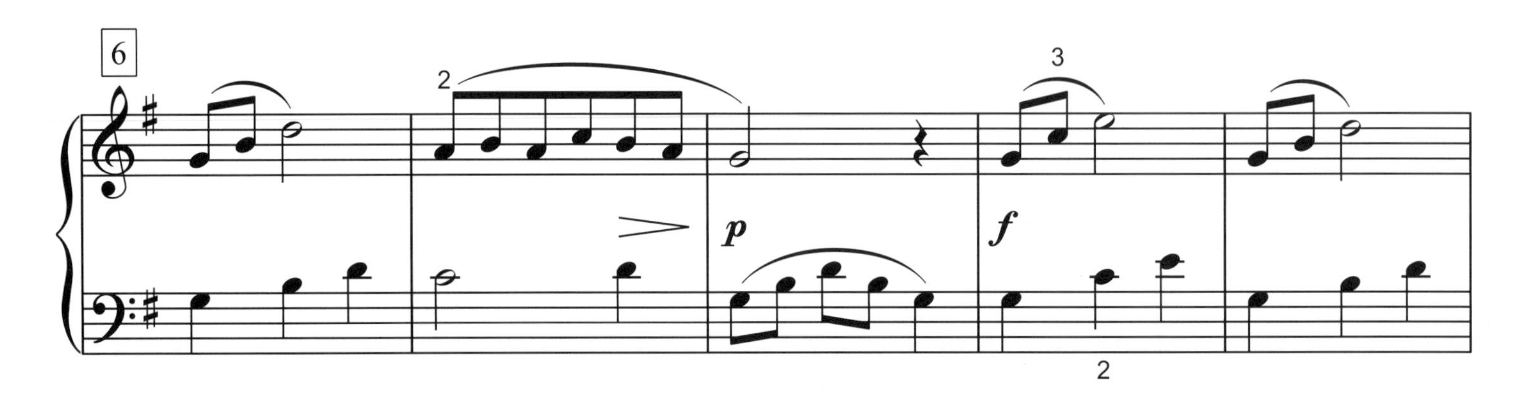

40.

Cornelius Gurlitt
Op. 187, No. 20

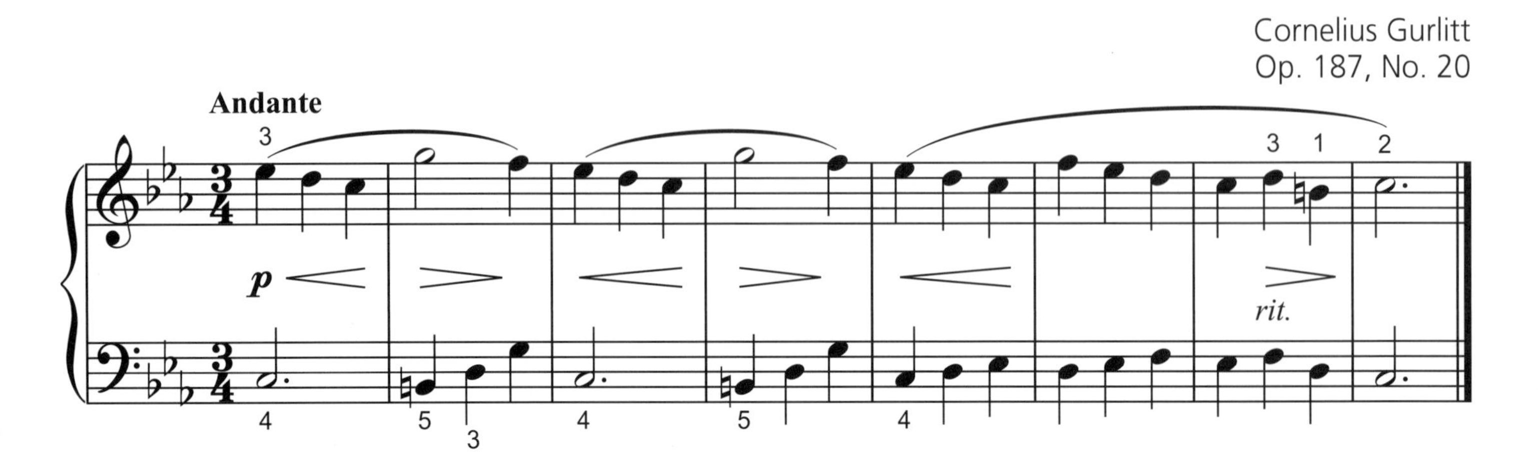

41.

Ferdinand Beyer
Op. 101, No. 64

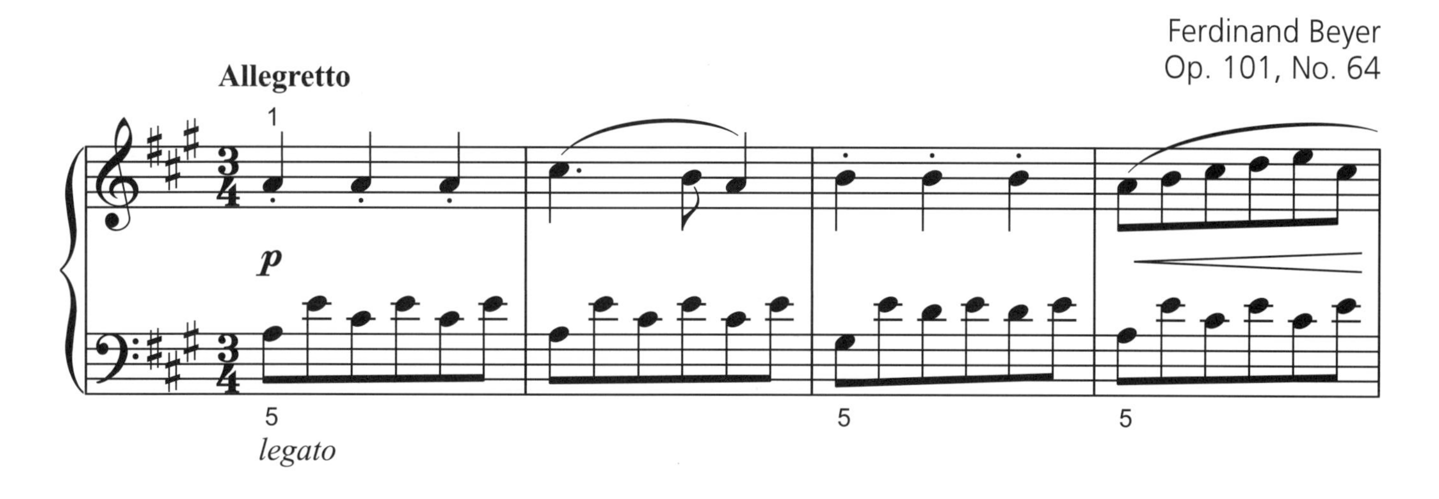

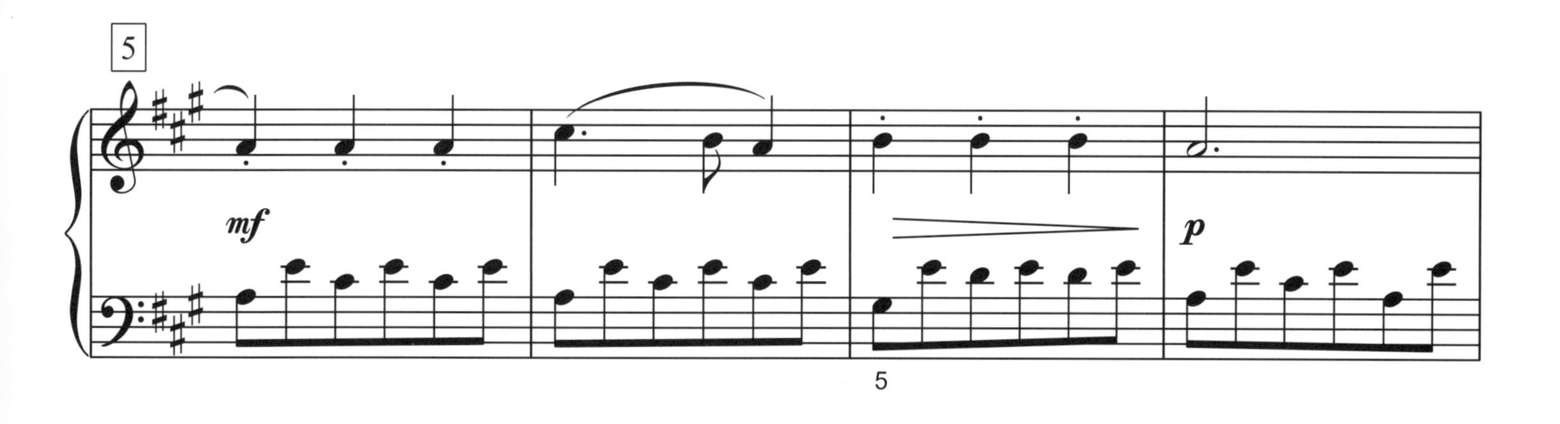

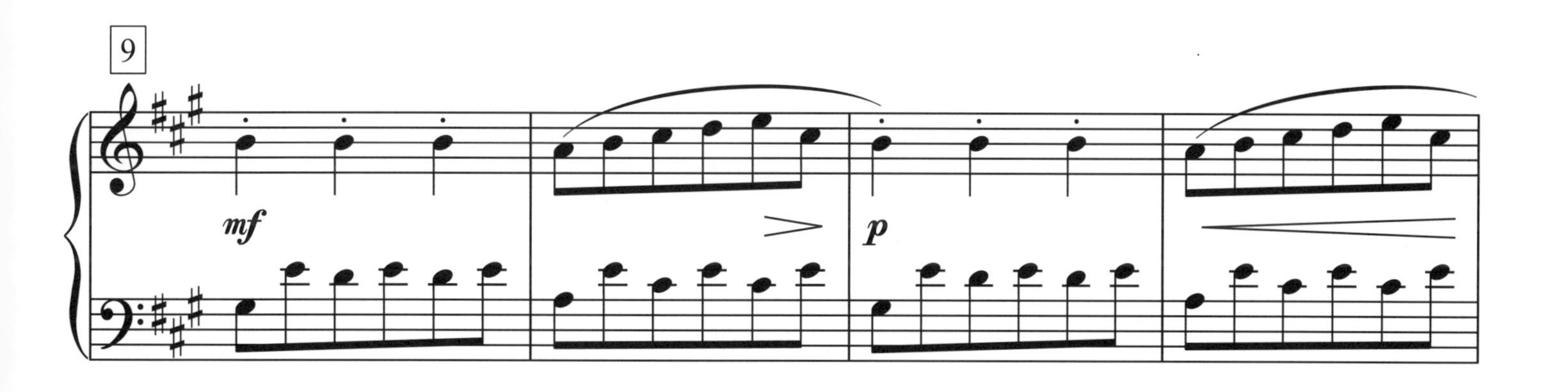

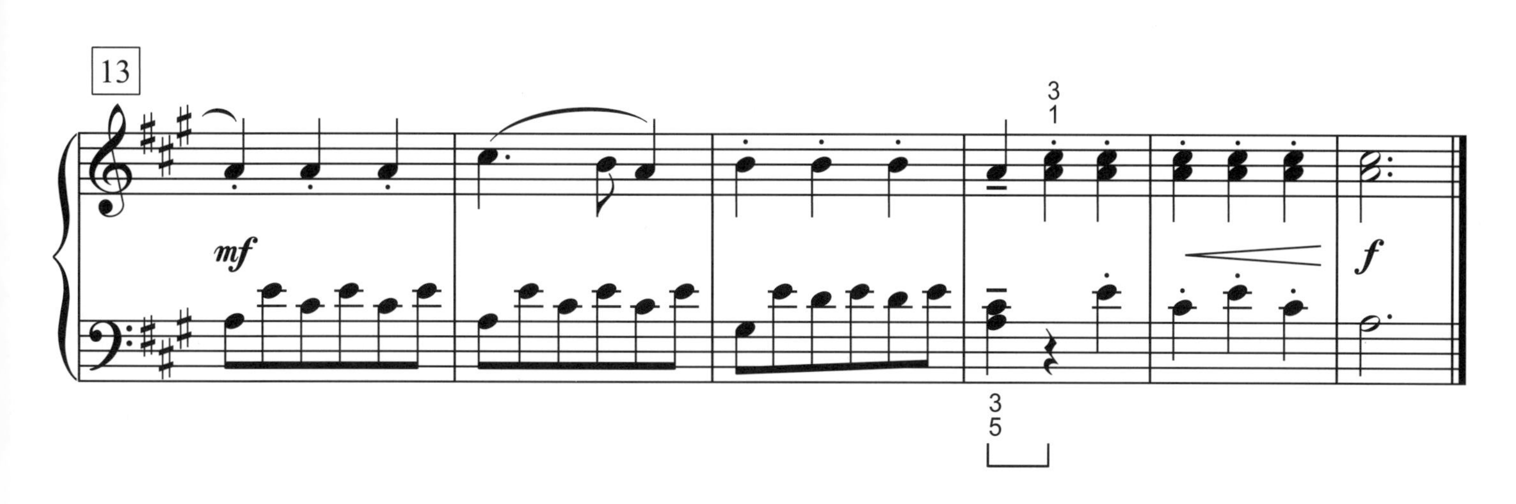

42.

Cornelius Gurlitt
Op. 82, No. 22

Allegro con spirito

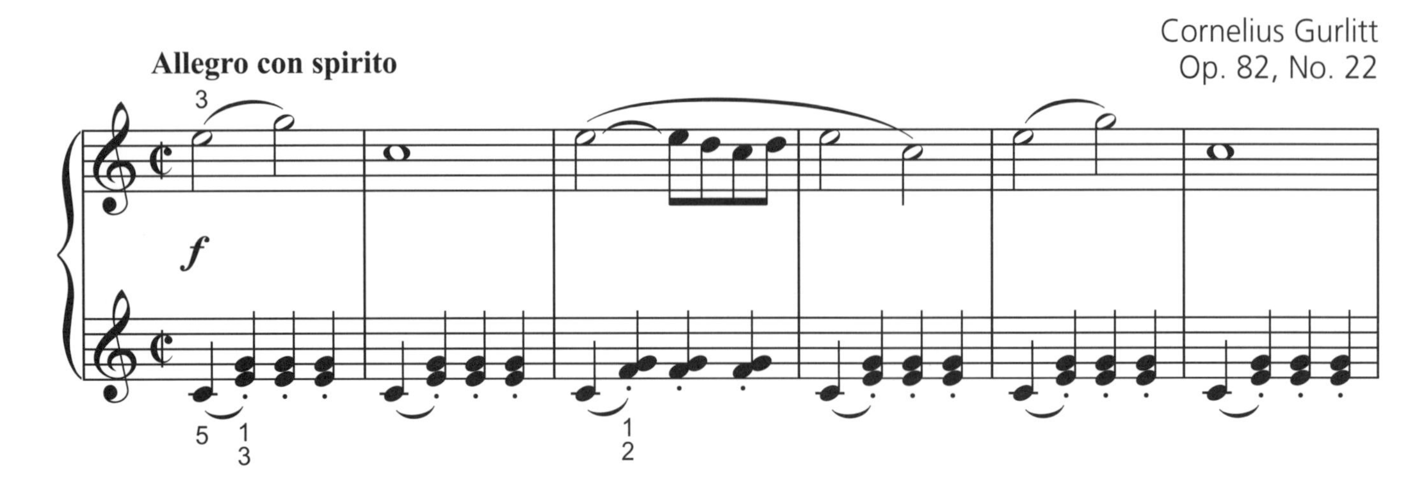

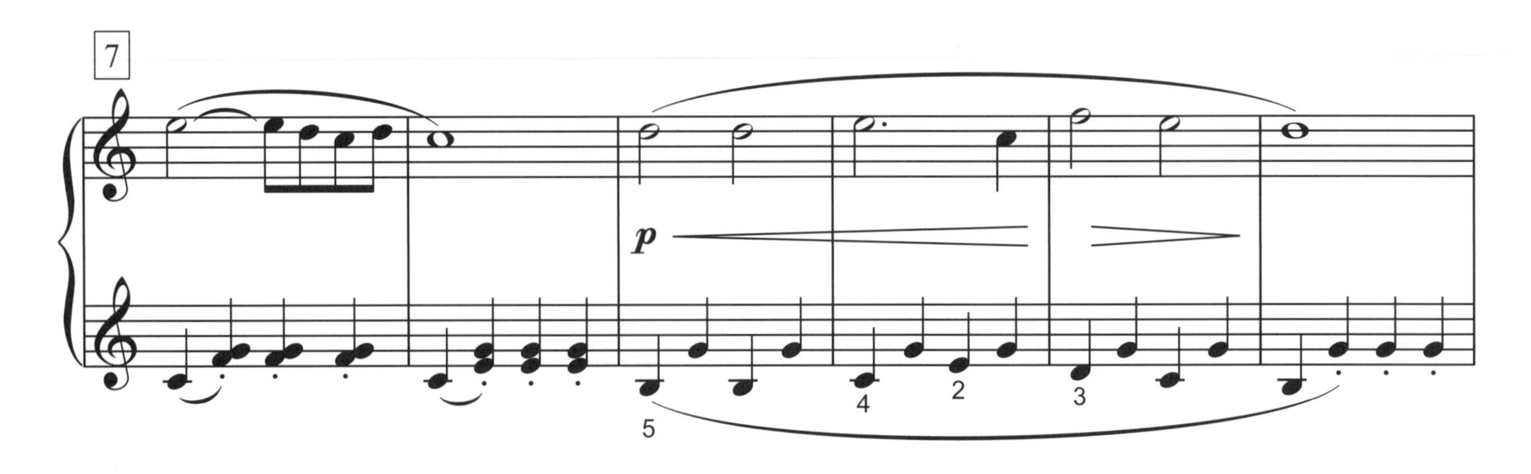

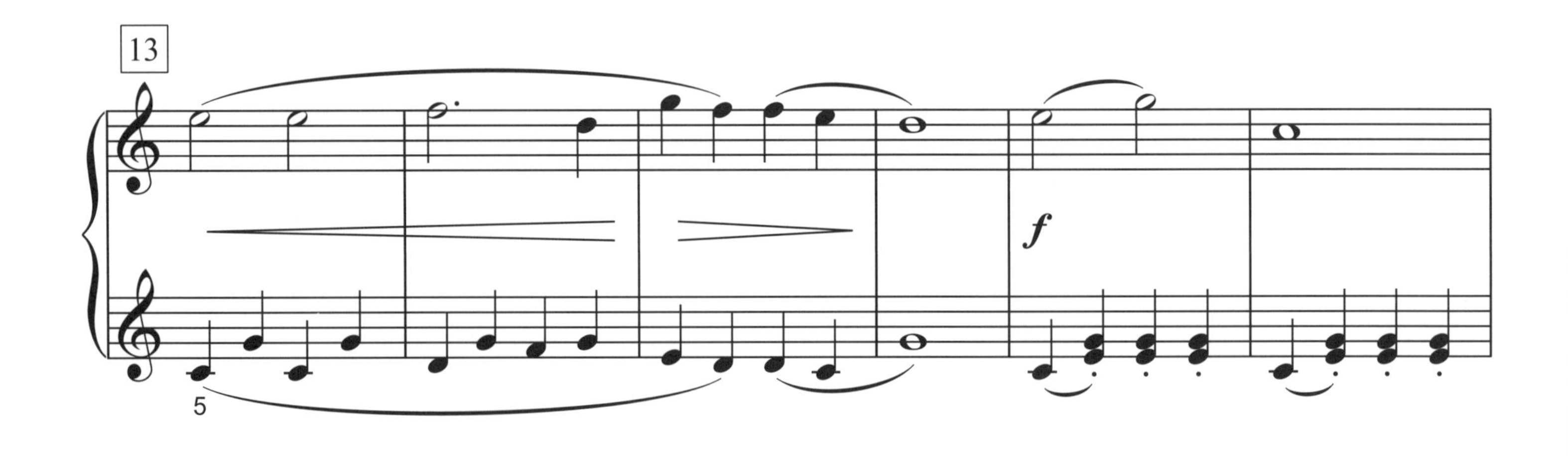

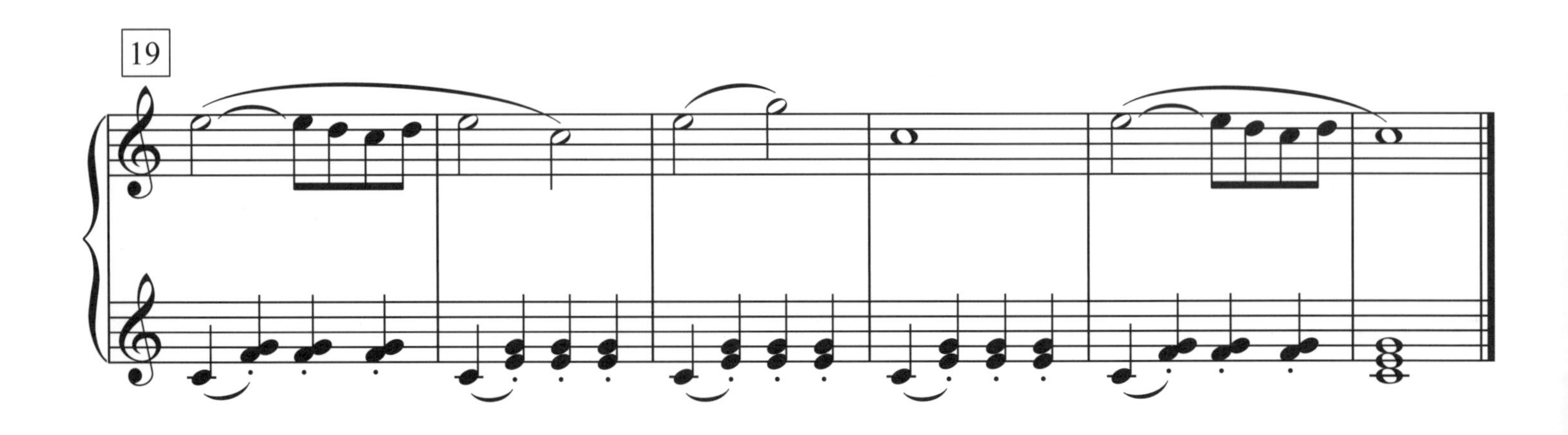

43.

Hermann Berens
Op. 70, No. 10

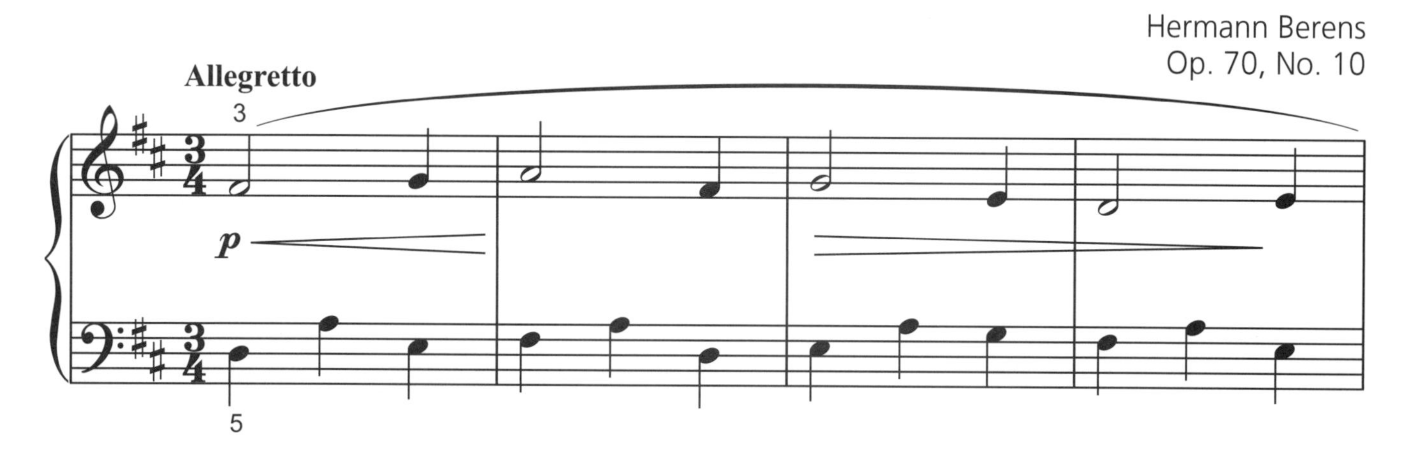

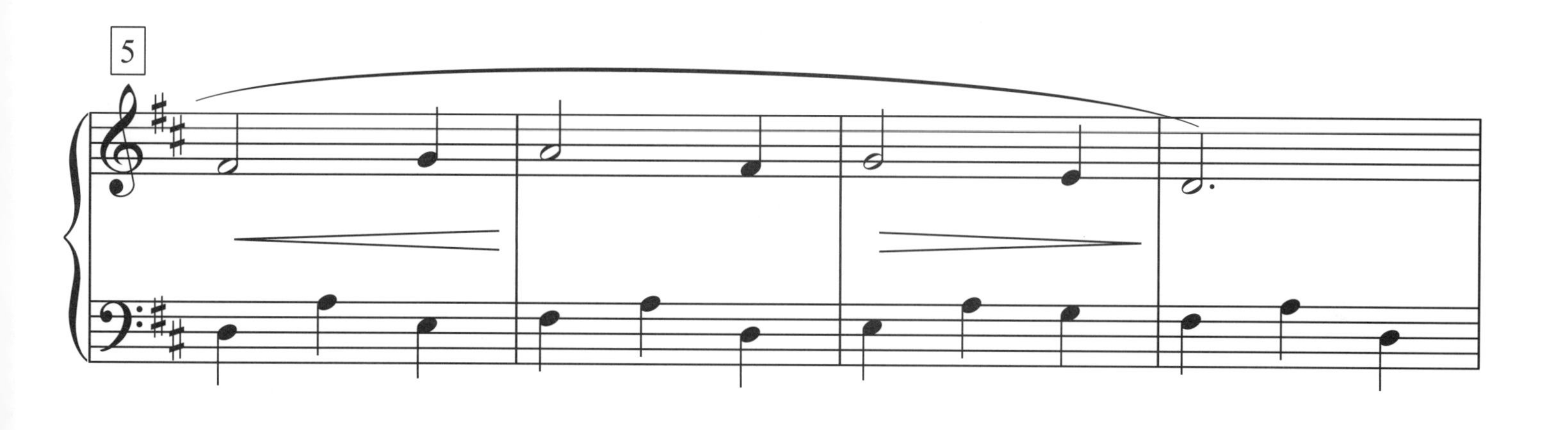

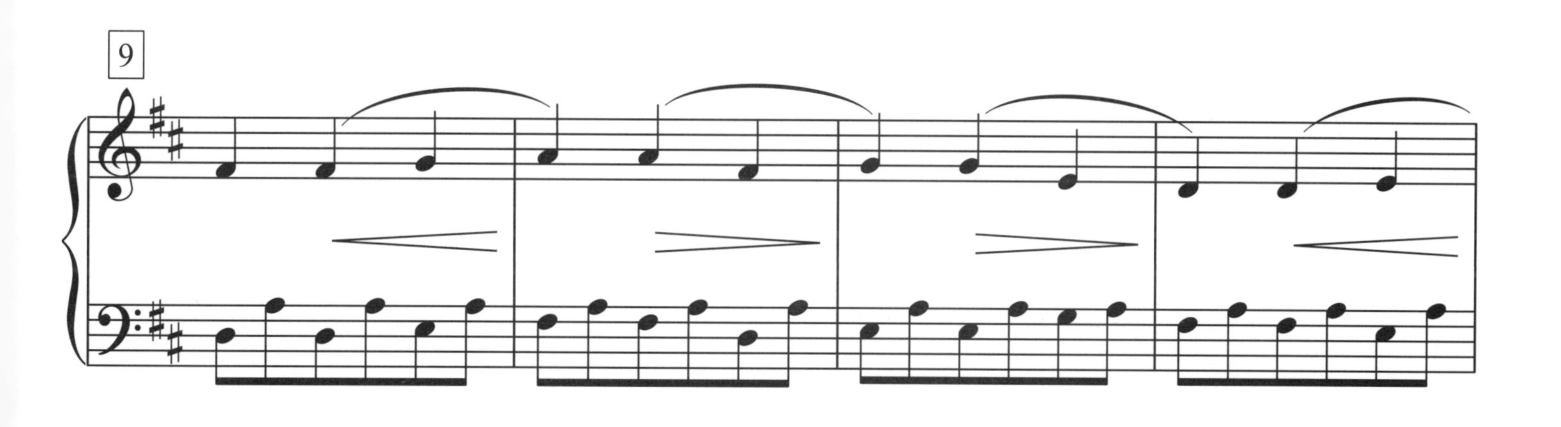

44.

Ludwig Schytte
Op. 108, No. 2

45.

Istvan Bartalus

46.

Cornelius Gurlitt
Op. 187, No. 21

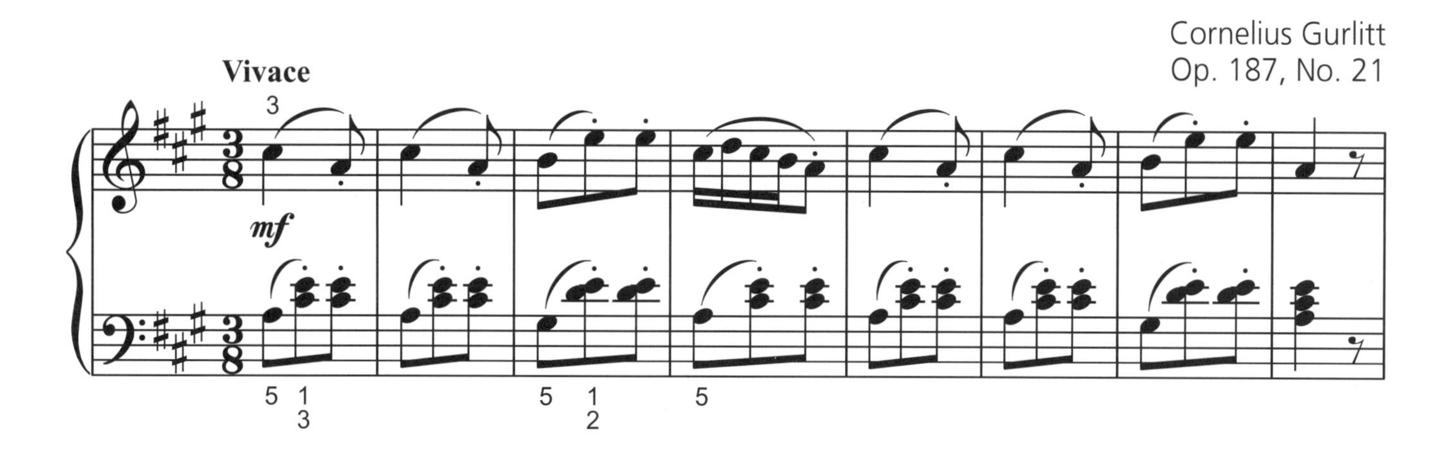

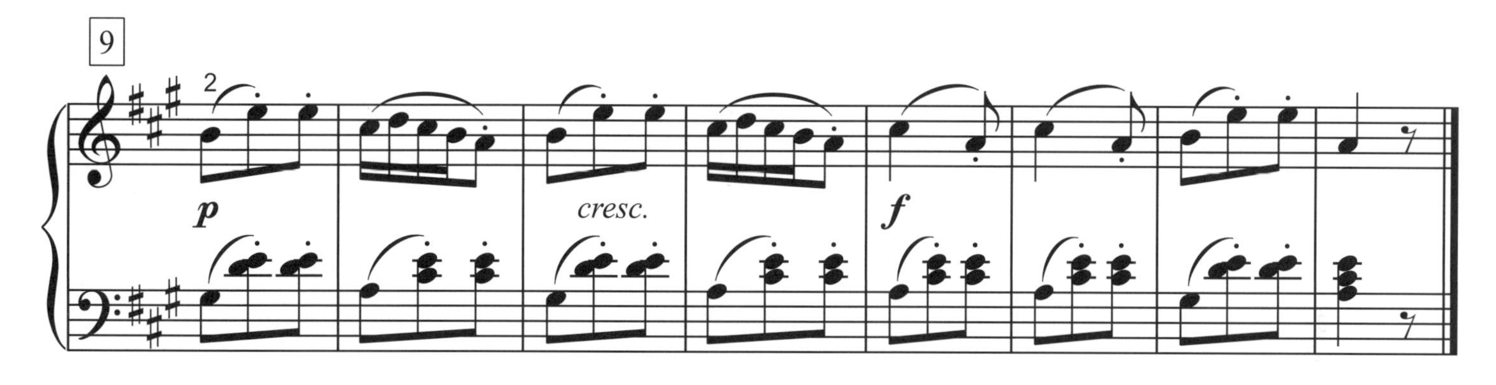

47.

Alexander Reinagle
Op. 1, No. 8

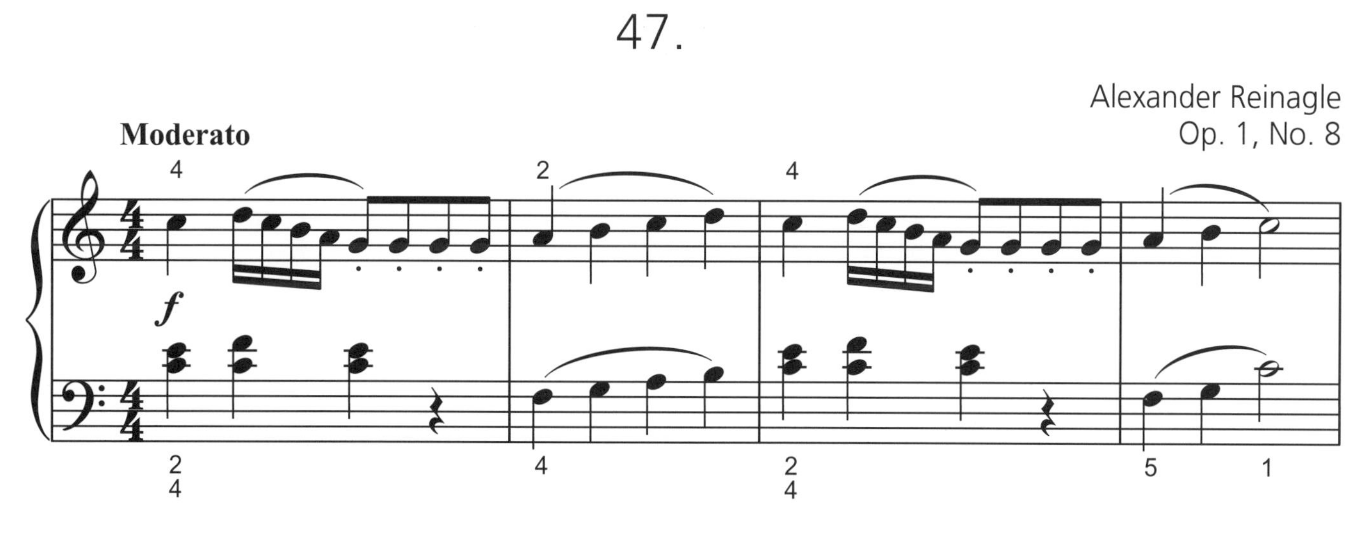

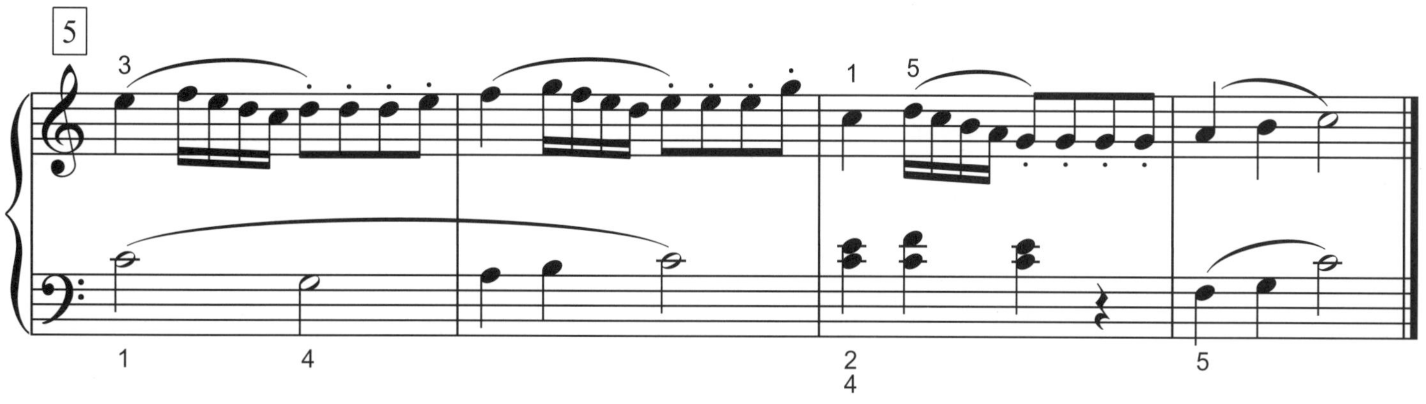

48.

48, 49, and 50 form one complete piece.

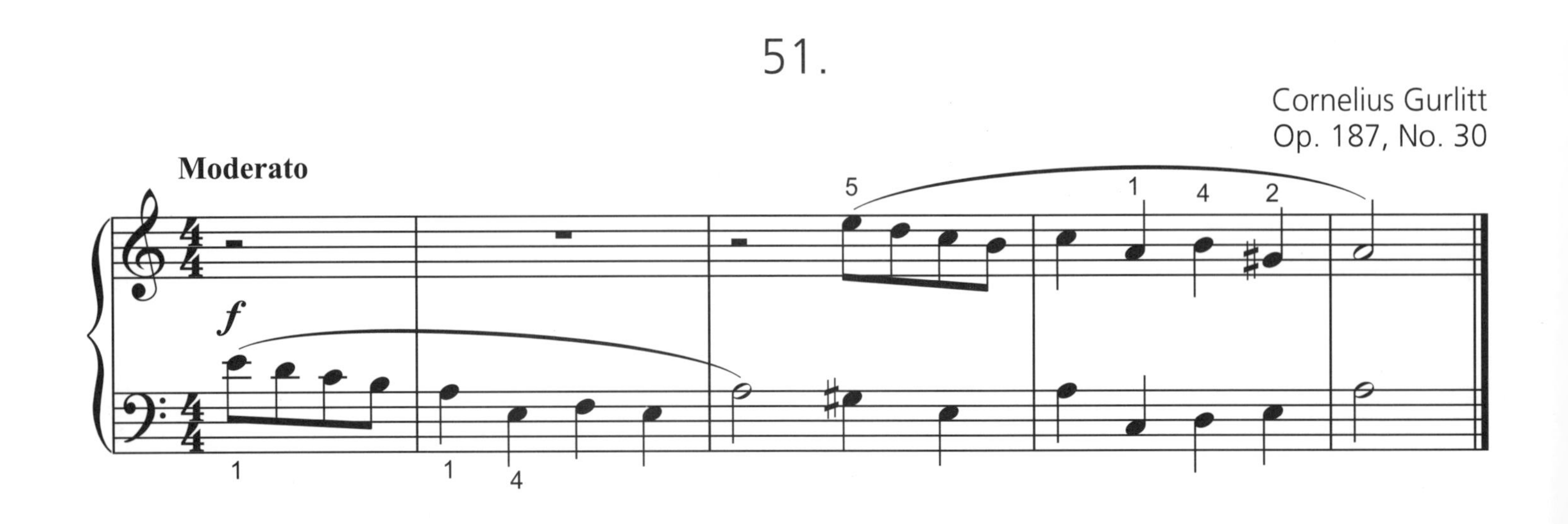

52.

Johann Georg Witthauer
(1750-1802)

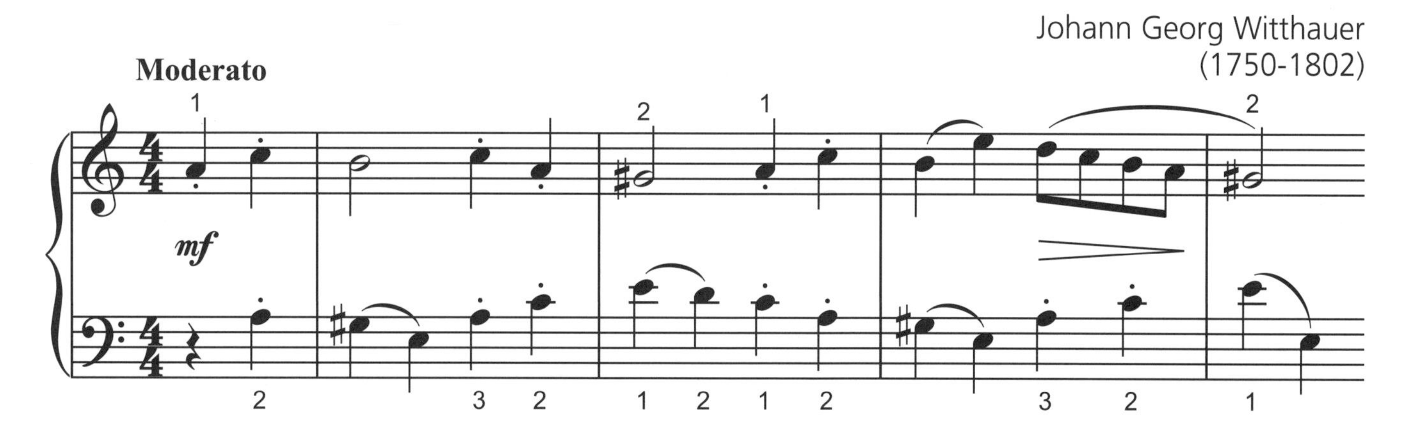

53.

Jan Jakub Ryba
(1765-1815)

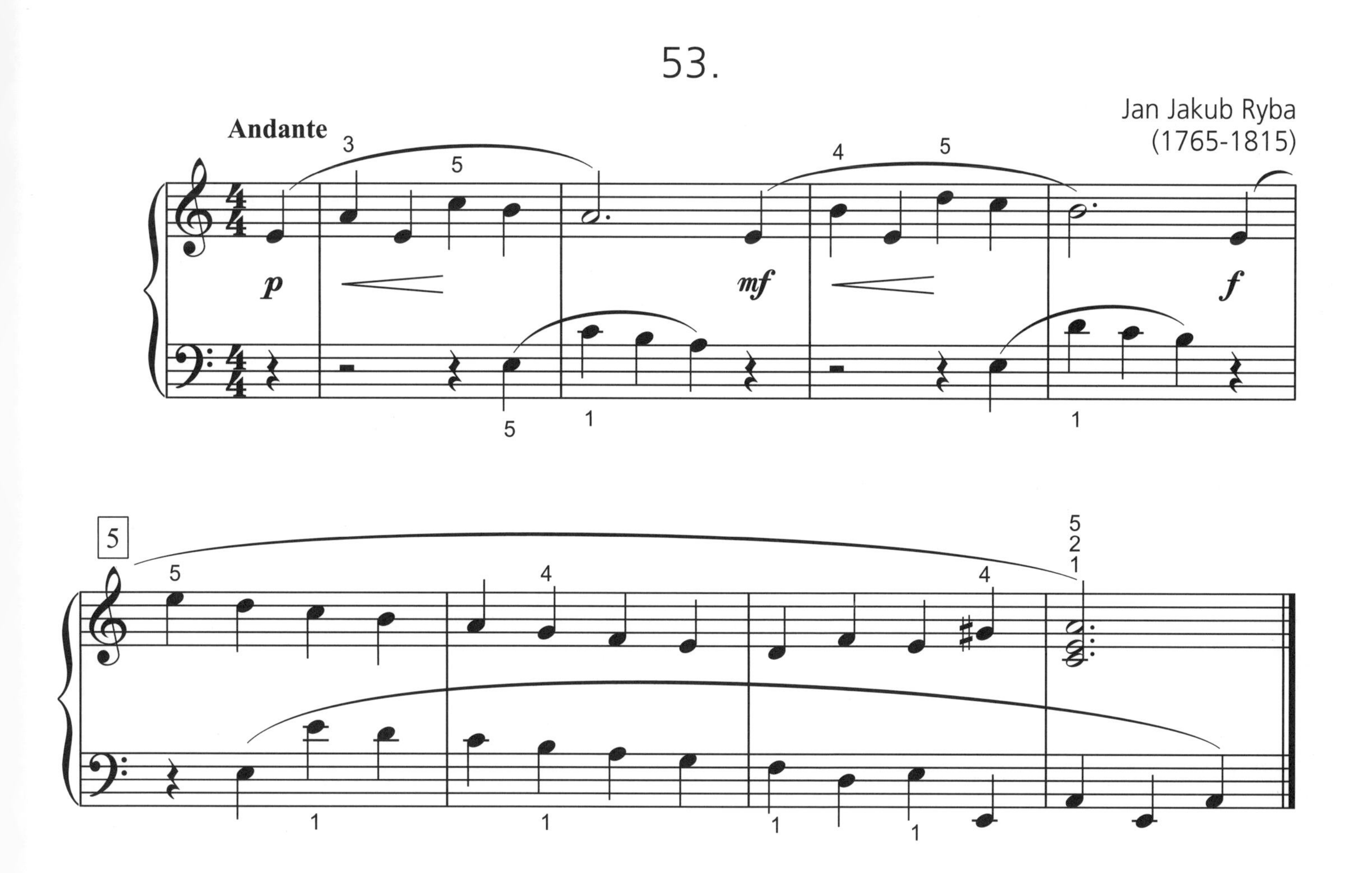

54.